Modern Publishing
A Division of Unisystems, Inc.
New York, New York 10022
Printed in Italy

Fisher-Price®

Rhyming ABC

Modern Publishing
A Division of Unisystems, Inc.
New York, New York 10022
Series UPC #: 39640

It's time to learn our ABCs.
Just look around you. It's a breeze!

To start the lesson, step this way.
Apples and ants begin with **A.**

Bs are everywhere you look.
Can you find blackboard, ball, and book?

Next comes **C**, for can and cup.
What other **C**s can you turn up?

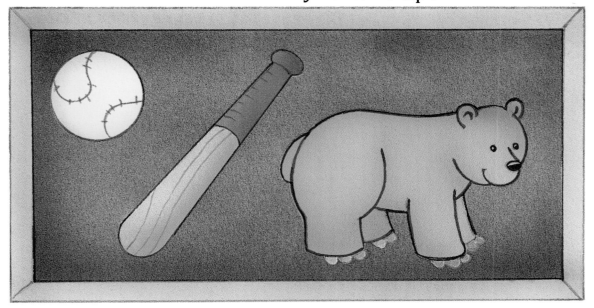

D's for desk and doll and door,
And other things. Can you find more?

E starts easel, elf, and ear.
Do you see other **E** words here?

F is fun. It stands for fish
And fairy, who can grant a wish.

Girl and game begin with **G**.
What other **G** words can you see?

H starts hand and also hook.
You'll find more **H** words if you look.
I's for iron; icebox, too,
And infant, just to name a few.

J's for jets that fly up high;
K's for kites that reach the sky.

Library begins with **L**;
Listen starts with **L** as well.

M's for magnet and for map;
N begins our daily nap.
O's for over. There's a light
Shining overhead too bright.
Turn the light off while we rest.
Darkness for a nap is best!

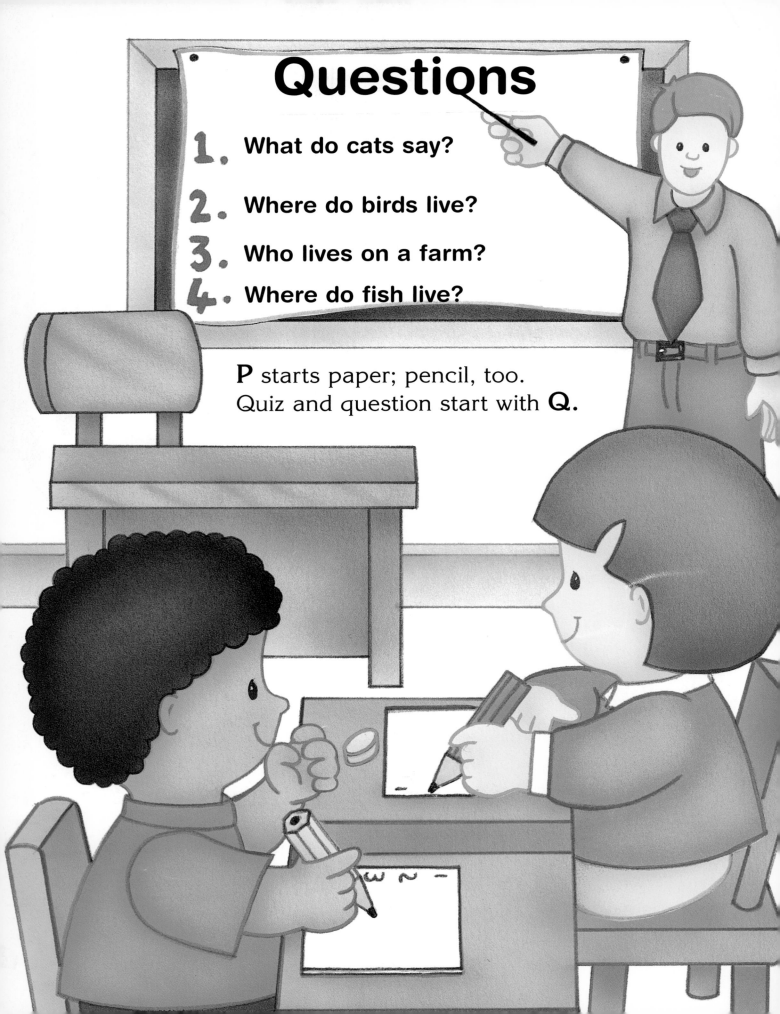

Questions

1. What do cats say?

2. Where do birds live?

3. Who lives on a farm?

4. Where do fish live?

P starts paper; pencil, too.
Quiz and question start with **Q.**

R's for read, recess, and rock.
S starts soccer, shoe, and sock.

T's for teacher, tape, and two.
Unicorn begins with **U**.

V's for violet, vase, and view.
Window starts with **W.**

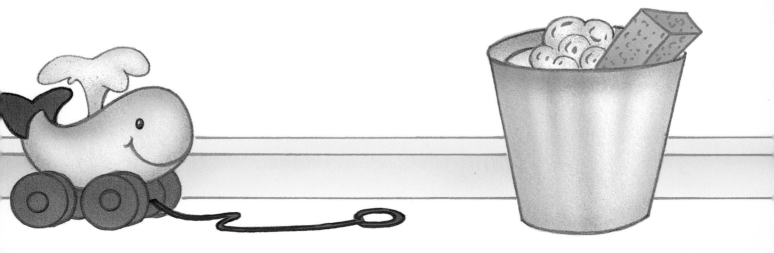

Xylophone begins with **X.**
Y for yo-yo comes up next!

Zip and zoom begin with **Z**s.
Now you know your ABCs!